The Du
Bridgewater - His Canal

Foreword

The first and still the definitive account of the history and growth of the Bridgewater Canal was written by Frank Mullineux and published by the Eccles and District History Society in 1959. In the last fifty years research has continued and other publications have amplified but not negated his work. However, as 2011 is the 250th anniversary of the opening of the Canal as far as Barton and the Aqueduct, the time has now come for a reassessment of the original publication although it still remains the best general source of information.

My thanks are due to my wife Maureen, Glen Atkinson and the late Ann Monaghan for valuable assistance in the preparation of this account and to Glen Atkinson for permission to use photographs from his collection.

I also wish to offer my sincere thanks to the Bridgewater Canal Company and the Peel Group without whose generous financial support this publication would not have been possible, and to Peter Nears for his patience and encouragement. I must also thank Jacqui Hutton of Salford City Council's Creative Services for her amazing forbearance and the design skills she has shown in the preparation of this book.

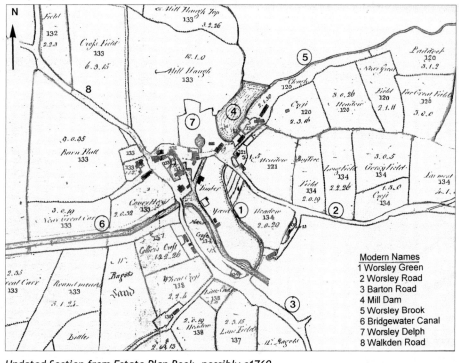

Undated Section from Estate Plan Book, possibly c1760

Modern Names
1 Worsley Green
2 Worsley Road
3 Barton Road
4 Mill Dam
5 Worsley Brook
6 Bridgewater Canal
7 Worsley Delph
8 Walkden Road

Published by The Bridgewater Canal Company, Peel Dome, Manchester M17 8PL

© 2011 by John Aldred

ISBN 978-0-9569403-0-8

Printed by Shanleys Limited, Units 38-39 Waters Meeting, Britannia Way, Bolton BL2 2HH

Contents

*View from under Worsley bridge, with Barton road bridge in the distance
(J.C. Nattes 1807)*

Introduction to
The Bridgewater Canal

By John Aldred

This is the story of the Bridgewater Canal, the most important of
the eighteenth century waterways that revolutionised transport
and industry in south-east Lancashire and particularly in the
area of Manchester and Salford. Most people know it as a strip
of orangey water surrounded by black and white buildings in the
heart of the village of Worsley which is situated some 12 Kms
west of Manchester, but it amounts to much more than that!

The name most associated with the Bridgewater Canal, which
originated in Worsley, is that of Francis, 3rd Duke of Bridgewater,
who was born in 1736 and died in 1803. A study of this kind might
perhaps therefore properly begin by tracing the background of
this remarkable man.

Part 1:

The Duke's Early Years

The 3rd Duke of Bridgewater, after whom the Canal is named, came of a long and sometimes noble lineage.

The Origins of the Family

At the time of the Norman Conquest, Worsley was part of the Manor of Barton and it is possible that a member of the Bridgewater family, having been given lands in Worsley and Little Hulton, adopted the name Elias of Worsley. Written evidence for the name begins in 1376 when one Geoffrey of Worsley was mentioned as "digging and selling sea-coles", an important product of the area. On his death the Manor passed into the hands of the Massey family but, in the 16th century, the male line of the Masseys died out and the estate passed to the Brereton family of Malpas in Cheshire. One Sir Richard Brereton, Lord of the Manor of Worsley, married Dorothy Egerton of Ridley in Cheshire, the first time the Egerton name appears in this complicated story, and when he died in 1598, his widow married Sir Peter Legh of Lyme Hall. Dorothy had an illegitimate half brother called Thomas Egerton, the offspring of her father with a serving maid. Despite this

The family took its name from Bridgwater in Somerset where the family once held estates.

irregularity, he prospered at Court and eventually rose to be Keeper of the Great Seal of England. This post was so prestigious that it made him only less important than the Royal Family and the Archbishop of Canterbury and he later became Lord Chancellor of England under James 1st. Thomas was the founder of the Canal Duke's branch of the family. He married three times and, in 1604, acquired the Ashridge estate near Berkhamstead in Hertfordshire. This estate has always remained a valued possession of the family. It was probably due to Dorothy's influence that the Worsley estates were granted to Thomas whose eldest son, John, was created 1st Earl of Bridgewater, when his father died in 1617. The family took its title from Bridgwater in Somerset where the family once held estates. From about 1600-1750 successive Lords of the Manor of Worsley did not live in Worsley but spent their time on their other estates.

The 4th Earl of Bridgewater, Scroop Egerton, the father of the Canal Duke, married Elizabeth Churchill who was the daughter of a couple who eventually became Duke and Duchess of Marlborough. Scroop hoped for a Dukedom but the Marlboroughs fell out of favour at Court so this did not come about. Scroop's wife died in 1714 and he married Rachel Russell. When George 1st came to the throne in 1714 Scroop came back into favour and was made Lord Chamberlain to the Princess of Wales; in 1720, he was created the 1st Duke of Bridgewater.

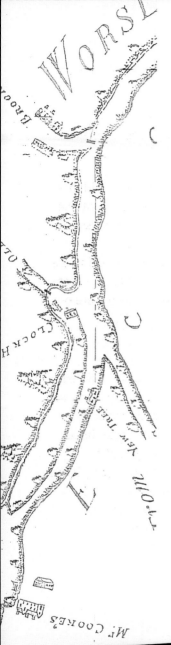

Scroop had eight children by his second wife and when he died in 1745, his wife showed little interest in her offspring and soon remarried. At the age of almost 50 years old she married a 26 years old man called Richard Littleton and settled in London to enjoy the good life. Most of the children did not long survive their father as tuberculosis was rife in the family. Francis' brother Charles died aged six, so Francis' elder brother John inherited the title, Duke of Bridgewater, in 1748. Francis' other brothers William and Thomas also died at an early age. Francis was sent off to a small boarding school possibly to avoid the contagion. Francis' three sisters all survived tuberculosis and married but unfortunately John, who had inherited the title, died from smallpox while at Eton and so Francis, aged eleven, became the 3rd Duke of Bridgewater. Neglected, starved of affection and fatherless, he must also have feared an early death. He quarrelled bitterly with his mother and step-father and left the family home. Francis went to stay with Samuel Egerton of Tatton although his legal guardians were the Duke of Bedford

Neglected, starved of affection and fatherless, he must also have feared an early death.

and Lord Trentham. Samuel Egerton later claimed guardianship as he received the rents and profits from the Worsley estates.

Egerton tried to placate Francis' mother but she, infatuated with her new husband, declared that she would not allow Francis back into her house until he agreed to make what she called "a proper submission" to her husband. Although he loved his mother, this, Francis was unwilling to do. Eventually, in 1749, sufficient funds were found in the family to enable Francis to go to Eton. Francis was bullied by his stepfather in the holidays and so his residence at Tatton became more or less permanent.

The Grand Tour

Francis had bouts of coughing and chest pains and it was feared that he might also die from tuberculosis. It was realised that if he survived to adulthood, he would become very wealthy and have control of many people and vast areas of land so it was decided that he should be given a thorough education. In those days this meant that he should be sent off on the Grand Tour. This was a method of completing the education of young men by sending them on an extended tour of Europe so that they could immerse themselves in the art and architecture, manners and traditions of a number of western and southern European countries.

Travels in France

In 1753, Francis was given into the charge of Robert Wood, traveller and classicist who also proved to be a kindly and patient man and set off for France. Their first stop was Paris. Here Wood tried to interest young Francis in reading and attending parties given in his honour by local ladies but without much success. Wood wrote in a letter to Francis' guardians that "He feared that the Duke would at any time prefer bad company to a good book"; fencing lessons did however raise some enthusiasm. From Paris they went to Lyons where Francis attended an Academy devoted to "intellectual training and rigorous instruction in riding and fencing". Francis liked it there and thought he would stay for a year. Sadly he and Wood fell out shortly after that and Wood threatened to resign because Francis ignored his advice and was keeping the "worst company". Wood relented after his salary had been increased and tried to interest Francis in female company, especially those "that had some Vices in which he might find his account".

Intellectual training and rigorous instruction in riding and fencing proved popular.

Sexual encounters for a sheltered youth were often regarded as an essential part of education whilst away from home. Despite finding himself a mistress whom Robert Wood feared he might marry, Francis eventually realised the error of his ways, began to learn French and reached an understanding with his tutor.

After a summer visit to Switzerland, by September 1753 they were back in Lyons. Francis decided that, rather than continuing with academic studies, he would like to see the Languedoc Canal, in southern France. This, together with its docks and locks, was already a tourist attraction. The Canal was about 150 miles long and took 8,000 workers nineteen years to build. It is likely that it was this visit that led to a life-long enthusiasm for canals and that it planted the seed from which, only five years later, the Bridgewater Canal was eventually to spring.

A Visit to Italy

Their next port of call was Italy but their departure from Nice was delayed because Francis had a cough, chest pains and a high fever. Fortunately Wood's family knew the Governor of Nice so Francis soon received medical attention and was able to recover in comfortable surroundings; "after two bleedings" or blood lettings they finally reached Rome. The Duke soon spent all his money and Wood had to lend him £400 to enable him to buy pictures and pieces of marble sculpture, many of which were sent back to England and left in unopened packing cases until after his death. These later became the foundation of the Bridgewater art collection.

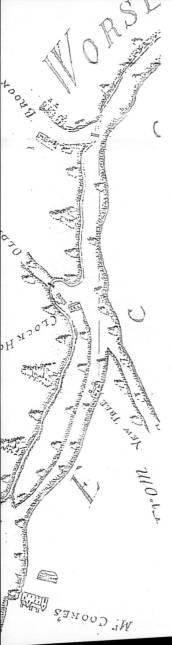

Fashionable life in Rome proved too much for Francis' delicate constitution and he again became ill; for weeks he hovered between life and death. By May 1755 he had started to recover but the doctors told him he must cut out his heavy drinking if his problems were not to recur.

A Young Man about Town

By September 1755 they were on their way home to England. Two years of foreign travel with the guidance of Robert Wood had changed the seventeen years old schoolboy into a nineteen year old who, although more worldly-wise, still had two more years to pass before he reached his majority. He passed the time by becoming a man about town in London free from the restraints of his tutor. He maintained a stable of race-horses from 1756-1770 and rode himself in some races under his own colours of blue and silver. He was 5 feet 9 inches (1.75metres) tall and though still in delicate health, racing and exercising his horses reduced his weight and helped his recovery.

He maintained a stable of race-horses from 1756-1770.

In order to maintain the Dukedom Francis had to have an heir and so needed to marry. When he was only sixteen, the Manchester Mercury was forecasting his marriage to Jane Revell, a wealthy heiress but Francis dithered so long that she eloped with a Cheshire squire. The nearest he came to marriage was with Elizabeth Gunning. The Gunning family was of impoverished Irish origins but the two daughters, Maria and Elizabeth were outstandingly beautiful. They were mobbed wherever they went much like modern "pop" stars. When they came to London, George II decreed

Wealthy heiress Jane Revell (Mullineux Collection)

that a platoon of the Guards should protect them from their admirers whenever they walked down the Mall on Sundays. Maria, the eldest, married the sixth Earl of Coventry and Elizabeth married the Duke of Hamilton. Hamilton died shortly afterwards leaving Elizabeth as a very wealthy widow.

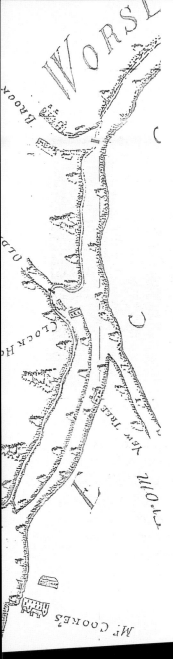

Although Francis was three years younger than Elizabeth he fell head over heels in love with her, proposed marriage and was accepted. Unfortunately, Elizabeth's sister, Maria began an affair with Lord Bolingbroke under her husband's nose and despite the laxity of morals at the time, this upset Francis. He wrote to his bride in the politest and most sensitive of terms asking that, in the circumstances, she should break off connections with her wayward sister. In her reply she insisted on having the privilege of deciding her own friends without interference from Francis. Francis back-pedalled, saying that he did not intend that she should sever all relations with her sister but the damage had been done.

Shortly afterwards it appeared that Elizabeth had actually been considering the attractions of the dashing Colonel Campbell, the future Duke of Argyll, for some time and her final

Although it caused him great distress, the engagement was ended.

The Gunning sisters walking in the Mall (Mullineux Collection)

letter to Francis was much the same as her first. The Duke took advice, was assured that his stance was correct and so, although it caused him great distress, the engagement was ended. Elizabeth and Campbell married in March 1759 and on the 4th of that month, Francis held a great ball at his London house. Some said this was a gesture made in an attempt to recover from his broken romance but there is also the possibility that it could have been a celebration for the passing of the third reading of his canal bill the previous week.

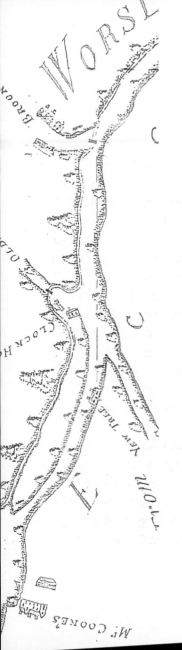

It has been said that the Duke lost all interest in female company following this affair but, in the Town and Country Magazine, it was claimed that on a visit to Salisbury, he attended a theatrical performance and realised that one of the actresses was the daughter of a tenant farmer on one of his estates. She had run away from home with the leading man of the company, been deserted and was destitute and hungry. He fed her at the inn where he was staying and, on hearing that her parents had died, he allowed her to live on a farm on his estate in Worsley. The gossips of the day suggested that she might have become his mistress but, if this was so, they were extremely discreet about it.

The combined net profit from the mines was only £122.

The Duke's Inheritance

The young Duke inherited substantial estates in twelve different counties of England stretching from Buckinghamshire in the south to Durham in the north. Despite this he would not have been regarded as wealthy by eighteenth century standards as he had very heavy financial commitments for salaries and maintenance. The estate which was to prove the most valuable of his properties was at Worsley, about 12 kilometres (approx 8 miles) west of Manchester. Coal had been mined here at least from mediaeval times. A document from 1376 records one of Sir Geoffrey Worsley's assets as "a profit in Worsley for digging and selling sea-coles was worth fifteen shillings a year". In 1428, three tenants, one called John the Colier, paid 6s 8d each for the "colemole" i.e. the right to mine coal. By the time of Scroop Egerton, Francis' father, most of the shallowest seams of coal had been worked out and shafts, still not very deep, were being dug. The drainage problem, which had always been severe, became worse in the new deeper shafts and the combined net profit from the mines was only £122, less even than profit from the Estate's farm rents. A sough, a drainage channel or tunnel cut into the side of a hill and continued at a slight angle until it reached the coal seams, seemed to be the best solution and one was begun in 1729 serving the Kingsway–Granville Street area of Worsley-Walkden, before the Bridgewater Canal.

Part 2:

The Transport Situation

The key to increasing output and distribution of coal from the Worsley area was transport. Packhorses that could carry about 125 kilogrammes (2½ hundredweight) of coal or carts which carried about 2 or 3 tons were the usual means of transport.

Transport Problems

Roads were often impassable. Arthur Young who visited the area in 1770 made the following observation "let me seriously caution all travellers who may accidentally purpose to travel this terrible country to avoid it as they would the devil, for a thousand to one but they break their necks or their limbs by over throws or breakings down, they will here meet with ruts which I actually measured, four feet deep and floating with mud only from a wet Summer. What therefore must it be after a Winter?"

"Let me seriously caution all travellers who may accidentally purpose to travel this terrible country to avoid it as they would the devil."

As early as 1721, the Mersey and Irwell Navigation had been given authority to make these rivers navigable and in 1737, an Act was passed to allow Worsley Brook to be made navigable which would have made it possible to carry boat-loads of coal from Worsley to the Irwell near Barton. Scroop Egerton was one of the Commissioners appointed to arbitrate between the promoters and other parties so it is unlikely that he was one of the actual promoters of the scheme. This plan was never implemented. In 1754, a group of Manchester business men sought powers to build a canal from Wigan and Leigh to Salford and they were supported by a petition from hatters, dyers, brewers, whitsters (bleacher of cloth), calenderers and other Salford and Manchester traders. There was opposition from the Turnpike Trustees and landowners but the idea was supported in the House of Commons Committee when it was told that the young Duke's guardian, Mr Egerton was in favour of the idea as he thought it "would be of advantage to His Grace through whose lands it would be carried". There is little doubt therefore that the idea of the canal as a way of improving the transport of coal and other goods was very much in the minds of local entrepreneurs at this time. An Act of 1755 had permitted the making of the Sankey Canal at St Helens; probably the first canal to be built in Britain in modern times and the young Duke must have been aware of the possibility of doing likewise. He had money and power but lacked the expertise to carry out his ideas.

By 1758, Francis Reynolds of Strangeways was writing to Edward Chetham that "The Duke of Bridgewater (Francis) is come into the country to visit his estate of Worsley, and does me the honour to take up his quarters with me... his Grace has found so large a Mine of Coal, for which he has so small a consumption, that he is inclinable to make a water road from Worsley Mill to Salford, at his own expense, by which means he will be able to supply Manchester at a much cheaper rate".

Early Attempts at Improvements

We have seen earlier that Francis was fascinated by the waterways he had seen on his Grand Tour and therefore it is not surprising that a "water road" as a means of supplying the vast needs of burgeoning industry in Manchester and Salford would

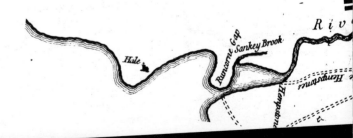

Map to right: The Bridgewater Canal in the 1760s

Francis was fascinated by the waterways he had seen on his Grand Tour.

have great appeal. The earlier schemes for developing this means of communication came to nothing and road transport, in 1758, was still the chief means for carrying goods in this part of Lancashire.

The setting up of Turnpike Trusts helped with the improvement of roads and in 1753 an Act of Parliament allowed a Trust to improve roads from Salford towards Wigan, Warrington, Bolton and Worsley and to charge tolls to their users; immediately the Mersey and Irwell Navigation offered lower rates for the transport of goods.

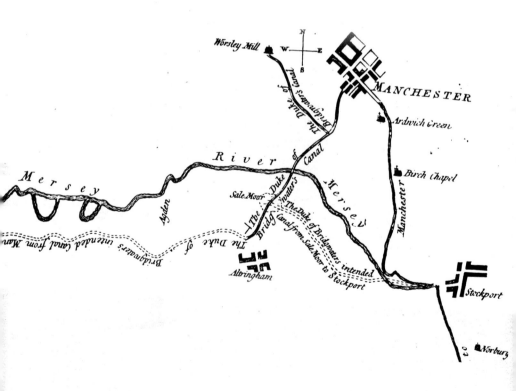

Part 3:

The Gilbert Era

John Gilbert
(Salford City Council)

The young Duke had the money but not the expertise. The Gilbert family of Staffordshire was to prove the answer. Thomas Gilbert, lawyer and Member of Parliament for Newcastle-under-Lyme and Litchfield was the Duke's General Agent during the 1750s. He had a younger brother called John who, unlike his elder brother, had been educated only at the village school near his home. John then went on to serve an apprenticeship with Matthew Boulton, the father of the Matthew Boulton who was famous for steam engines and the Soho works in Birmingham. Matthew senior made buttons so John Gilbert probably gained more during this period by learning about business than technical skills.

John Gilbert in Worsley

By 1753 John was working for the Duke of Bridgewater under his elder brother Thomas but in 1757, Thomas had to move back to the family estate and John became manager of the Worsley enterprises. In 1757, Francis Egerton, 3rd Duke of Bridgewater was 21 and John Gilbert 33 years of age. John moved

John Gilbert was an adventurous entrepreneur in his own right.

to Worsley with his wife and family in 1757 and what was to be a remarkable partnership lasting over forty years had begun. Apart from playing a major part in the design and construction of the canals, John Gilbert was an adventurous entrepreneur in his own right. He had interests in a number of industries in the north of England including copper and lead mining, farming the Worsley estate, the creation of a drainage scheme for a large part of Martin Mere in West Lancashire, salt mining in Cheshire and graphite mining in Cumbria which was linked to a business in Worsley making black-lead pencils and cleaning materials. These were all businesses requiring a good deal of travel but he was never accused of neglecting his work for the Duke; indeed the Duke was often involved in his ventures.

Thomas asked his brother to inspect the mines at Worsley and suggest ways in which they could be made more profitable. They realised that there was a market of about forty thousand people and a great deal of industry in the Manchester and Salford area desperate for cheaper coal but development depended on radical improvements in the drainage of the coal seams to increase production and improvements in the transport system to enable coal to be carried more easily to markets. John Gilbert retired to the Bull Inn in Salford to consider the situation without interruption. Eventually he came up with a plan. He realised that if tunnels large enough to carry boats laden with coal could be drilled into the rock northwards from Worsley Delph until they intersected the steeply dipping coal measures under Walkden Moor, coal could be taken direct from the workings to the Delph and so by a surface canal to markets in Manchester. This underground canal would also help to solve the drainage problems.

Part 4:

Canal Construction

In the eighteenth century, schemes such as the building of the Bridgewater Canal had to be approved by Parliament.

Parliament and Canals

Firstly the scheme had to be put to a Committee of MPs usually with interests in the district and then, often after having been modified, the matter went to the House of Commons for their approval. If successful, the Bill then went to the House of Lords and only after it had received their approval did the Bill go to the Sovereign for his consent.

The Duke was delighted with Gilbert's ideas and progress on the planning of the surface canal was quickly made. Much of the planning took place in the eastern rooms of Worsley Old Hall, which can still be seen.

Planning took place in the eastern rooms of Worsley Old Hall.

The first Canal Act 1759

In December 1758, two petitions in support of the plan to build a canal from Worsley to Salford were presented to the House of Commons, one from the "Gentlemen Traders and Manufacturers residing near Hollin Ferry, and in Lymm and Thelwell" and the other by the "Gentlemen, Traders and Manufacturers in the Towns of Manchester and Salford". The scheme was placed before the House of Commons Committee appointed to discuss the plans by the Duke's solicitor, William Tomkinson and John Gilbert, who gave the technical details as to route and water supply. One of the points in favour of building the canal was that the Duke pledged to deliver coal at "not exceeding four pence per Hundred" as against 7d or 8d (3p) per hundred (pounds weight) charged at the time. The Act received Royal Assent in March 1759 and work on digging the canal began soon after.

James Brindley comes to Worsley

John Gilbert was an excellent land agent and accountant who also had training as an engineer but obviously the services of an experienced practical engineer who was also experienced in water control were required. Such a man was James Brindley. James Brindley was born in 1716 at Tunstead near Buxton. At the age of seventeen he was apprenticed to a mill-wright and learned a great deal, often by his own efforts, about water mechanisms. In 1752 Brindley was employed to drain the sodden Wet Earth colliery at Clifton and this he did by inventing an innovative scheme. This involved building a 731 metres (800 yards) long mill race which took water from the Irwell underground, under the river itself, and so generated a large head of water further down stream, where it reappeared, which was used to drive pumps which drained the colliery. This scheme and other work for the family commended James Brindley to John Gilbert

James Brindley

who introduced him to the Duke in sometime about May 1759. 'Schemer' Brindley as his friends called him was received as an honoured guest and was the ideal man for the job. He was innovative and of strong character and was employed as a consultant engineer who brought with him a small group of skilled workmen.

Construction Begins

The 1759 Act canal was planned to run from Worsley to Salford on the north side of the River Irwell and to Hollin Ferry on the River Mersey, avoiding locks by following the 82 foot (c 25 metre) contour. Work soon began on the surface canal, on the underground canal from the Delph, and a canal westwards into Chat Moss in the direction of Hollin Ferry. It is thought possible that Salford had never really been planned as the canal's final

He produced a large Cheshire cheese from which he proceeded to carve a model.

destination. Plans were soon developed to alter the route to cross the Irwell by an aqueduct and continue the canal into the heart of Manchester where the largest markets existed. It is also possible that plans were in mind, for the future, to continue the canal westwards to Liverpool.

The second Canal Act 1760

Radical alterations such as these needed a further Act of Parliament and on the 25th January 1760, the Duke presented his petition. There was much opposition from the Toll Road Commissioners but also massive support from businesses and local people from around Altrincham. This time it was James Brindley who presented the details to the Committee. He proved to be a powerful advocate who, when members were bemused by the idea of being able to build a barge-carrying aqueduct across the River Irwell, produced a large Cheshire cheese from which he proceeded to carve a model. When questions were asked about the waterproofing of the trough, he demonstrated how sand and clay mixed with water and well compacted could prove completely waterproof. As usual the administrative work for the canal bid was done by John Gilbert who received extra pay for his efforts. With evidence such as that of James Brindley and powerful backers, the second Act made its way through both Houses of Parliament and received Royal Assent in March 1760.

The Barton Aqueduct

Canal digging in the eighteenth century was a matter of picks, shovels, wheelbarrows and hard labour and a labour force of about 400 men was employed on the project. The most ambitious part of the scheme was the building of the aqueduct at Barton. Built of stone, the main section had three arches with stop gates at each end to seal off the

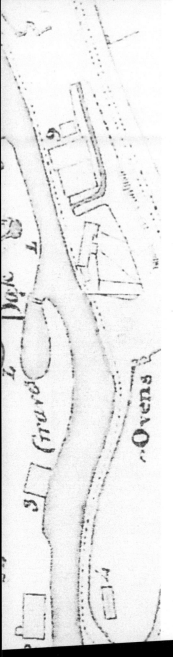

aqueduct should repairs be required and there were sluice gates on the aqueduct itself so that, if necessary, it could be emptied once the stop gates had been closed. There were also two shorter aqueducts, one over Barton Lane on the north side and another on the south side over the lane to Barton Corn Mill. When water was finally let onto the aqueduct, to Brindley's horror, one of the arches on the section over the Irwell began to buckle. Brindley, who had been overworking for weeks and drinking heavily, panicked and had a nervous breakdown. He retired to bed at the Bishop Blaize tavern in Stretford leaving the aqueduct to its fate. John Gilbert came to the rescue.

It appeared that Brindley had put too much weight on the sides of the arches so Gilbert had the lining clay removed and "puddled" it again. Fortunately this solved the problem and on 17th July 1761 the Duke was able to invite

Brindley had put too much weight on the sides of the arches so Gilbert had the lining clay removed.

View of Barton Bridge (Mullineux Collection)

a number of friends to see the aqueduct filled and a barge carrying 50 tons of coal cross it without incident. The aqueduct was to remain in place for over 100 years, although it had to be rebuilt after flood damage in 1822-1824, before being replaced by the Barton Swing Aqueduct across the Manchester Ship Canal, which still exists today.

Once the aqueduct was completed, construction of the Canal towards Manchester continued rapidly. Coal was being sold at Cornbrook, about a mile from Manchester in 1773 and in the city itself by 1774 at 3½d per basket of about 140 pounds weight (63.6 kilogrammes) cheaper even than the price of 4d laid down in the Act.

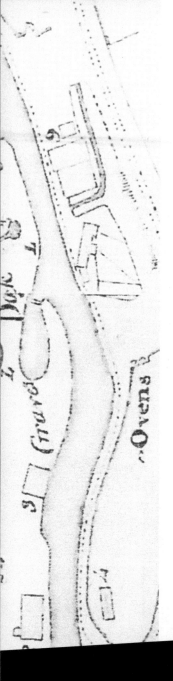

The third Canal Act 1762

Even before the Aqueduct was complete, plans were being prepared for a further extension of the Canal into Cheshire. This would involve a third Act of Parliament and would also involve some difficult engineering. A massive embankment would have to be built across Sale Moor and another across the valley of the Bollin if locks were to be avoided. There would also be a need for a much larger canal terminus in Manchester. There was a great deal of opposition from competing modes of transport in the district. Objections were raised especially by The Old Navigation on the River Irwell who had struggled for thirty seven years to provide a satisfactory means of transport on the River despite periods of low water and other problems. The Duke was quick to point out these shortcomings in his proposals for the new extension to the Bridgewater Canal.

This third Act also brought another famous engineer onto the scene.

This third Act also brought another famous engineer onto the scene. John Smeaton, designer of the Eddystone lighthouse, was called as an expert witness. He was a member of the Royal Society and a nationally known figure whose views were taken note of. His evidence was to do with water supply for the new canal, which was a key factor in permission being granted. The Old Navigators were frightened that the new canal would take away some of their sources of water thus worsening their problems in times of drought. Smeaton reassured the Committee that river levels would not be affected. Smeaton's evidence was followed by that of James Brindley. The Duke equipped Brindley with a new suit, breeches, shoes and buckles before he attended the Committee and his evidence was again to do with locks and water supply. The Duke also sent out 750 letters to MPs, influential people and those still to be convinced, to encourage them to support the Bill.

The Aqueduct crossing Barton Lane 1770 (A. Young)

The canal basin at Castle Field, Manchester 1807 (J.C.Nattes)

This did not entirely solve the problems of getting permission to cross the land of the large landowners in the area. Sir Richard Brooke of Norton Priory was the major protagonist, demanding exorbitant amounts of money for relatively small pieces of land. Disputes with landowners through whose land the canal would be cut caused great delays but eventually problems were solved, the Parliamentary Committee was convinced and the Act passed on 24th March 1762.

The Duke's troubles did not end with the passage of the Act. At the Manchester terminus of the Canal, the Duke had to purchase the

A crane worked by a water wheel was able to hoist boxes of coal to street level.

Hulme Hall estate for £9,000 to obtain the land needed for wharves and warehouses. A canal basin was built together with warehouses owned by the Duke and a company called Henshall and Gilbert, who were carriers.

John Gilbert was a partner and Henshall was James Brindley's brother-in-law. A lime kiln and a brick works were also built together with an ingenious device for the speedy unloading of coal barges. This, described by Arthur Young, Secretary to the Board of Agriculture, who visited Worsley in 1770, was a crane worked by a water wheel which was able to hoist boxes of coal to street level from barges which had travelled along a specially dug tunnel to a point underneath a hole in the road where there was a hoist. Using this method, an early example of containerisation, two men and a boy could unload a cargo of 5 tons in twenty or twenty five minutes.

Later a tunnel, known as the "Duke's Sough", was dug to carry boatloads of coal to a point near London Road on the Ardwick side of Manchester.

A massive flight of ten locks was opened in 1773, the only ones on the Bridgewater Canal, to allow canal traffic to enter the River Mersey at Runcorn. Difficulties with the terrain meant that it was not until 1776 that this section of the canal was finally opened.

Sadly James Brindley did not live to see the completion of his work; he died in 1772 at the age of 56 years. He not only worked on the Bridgewater Canal but together with his partners, assisted with over twenty other schemes in many other parts of the country.

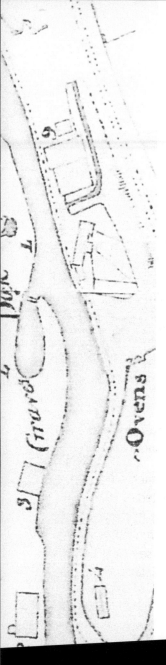

End of Canal Construction

Although the Duke had had a dock at the Runcorn end of the Canal since 1773, a new larger dock was completed in 1791 and celebrations included an ox roasting for all the "navigators". After much opposition from the Corporation of Liverpool the Duke was allowed to build a dock, known as the Duke's Dock, in the centre of the city. Warehouses for goods arriving and departing by sea were also constructed.

The fourth Canal Act 1795

The fourth and last Canal Act of the Duke was passed in 1795 and this allowed an extension of the Bridgewater Canal to be built from Worsley to Leigh in 1821. Here it eventually joined up with the Leeds-Liverpool Canal and via that, to the Lancaster Canal. This gave access to Liverpool from Manchester without having to wait for the tide in the Mersey estuary. Once again there were objections from landowners but by now the benefits of canals were generally well understood and these objections were overcome. The Canal

Truly a major contribution to the British transport system.

Painting of Barton Aqueduct by French Philosopher Jean Jacques Rousseau 1766 (Mullineux Collection)

was completed by 1800 but it was not until 1821, after the Duke's death that it linked up with the Leeds-Liverpool Canal.

At last the Canal system was complete, thirty two years from its beginnings in or near Worsley Delph. It finally consisted of 40 miles of waterways which in Manchester linked up with the Rochdale Canal. Near Preston Brook it linked with the Grand Trunk (Trent and Mersey) Canal and at Runcorn it joined the River Mersey. Near Leigh it connected with the Leeds-Liverpool Canal. Truly a major contribution to the British transport system.

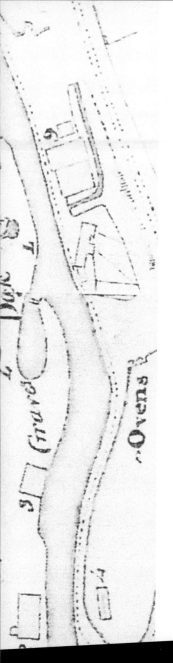

The success of the Duke's enterprises encouraged other people to consider canal building and eventually the Rivers Trent, Mersey, Thames and Severn were all linked by canals.

Financial Problems

All these provisions and the passage of the Act were very expensive and the Duke was constantly short of money. John Gilbert was often given the job of trying to borrow money, even as little as £5 from farmers on the estate and the Duke cut his own expenditure to £400 a year. He borrowed £300 from Robert Lansdale, his cashier, despite the fact that his salary was only £100 a year and even this was lent to the Duke at 5% interest. Later the Duke was able to borrow from Messrs Child and Co of London on the security of the Worsley Canal, which, by that time, was recognised as being a sound investment.

The success of the Duke's enterprises encouraged other people to consider canal building.

Worsley Works Yard in the 19th century - now Worsley Green

A Strange Encounter

One day when John Gilbert was on his way to try to borrow money
from some of the Duke's more remote tenants, he met a stranger on
a superb horse. In conversation the stranger proposed exchanging
his fine animal for John's very ordinary steed. Perhaps surprisingly,
John agreed to the exchange which was certainly to his advantage.
Later John called at an inn for refreshment where he was greeted
by the landlord in a very familiar way. This surprised John as he had
never visited the inn before. His surprise deepened when the landlord
asked him if his saddlebags were full. Suddenly it dawned on John
that he had changed horses with a famous highwayman who wished to
exchange his well-known horse for a more anonymous animal; whether
he kept the horse is not known!

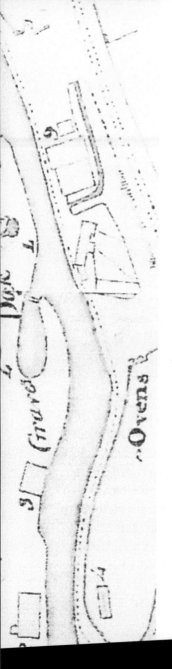

Industrial Development at Worsley

The hub of the Canal and coalmining network was Worsley and rapid industrial development took place in the centre of the village especially on the area now known as Worsley Green. By 1780, a massive warehouse was built on the bank of the Canal equipped with a huge crane on one corner enabling it to lift heavy loads from barges. Boat builders, joiners, carpenters, sawyers, masons, nail makers, sailmakers and many other trades were set up. The whole area now known as Worsley Green was covered with industrial buildings. In 1773 Josiah Wedgwood, of pottery fame, visited Worsley and wrote in his diary "We visited Worsley which has the appearance of a considerable seaport town". An important group of dry docks was built on the edge of the Canal at Worsley. Boats sailed into the dock, the gates were closed and the dock emptied. A solution had to be found to the problem as to how to empty the dock as the water levels inside and out were equal. A unique solution was found and a plug was built into the side

"We visited Worsley which has the appearance of a considerable seaport town".

of the dock. When the plug was lifted, water cascaded down into the Worsley Brook which ran in a culvert under the Canal at this point. Both dock and plug are still in use in the 21st century.

Between Barton Road and the Canal at the southern edge of the village, a large lime kiln was built. Large quantities of lime were needed for fertiliser and for mortar to be used in building on the estate. Fortunately John Gilbert had experience of lime burning before he came to Worsley and supplies of Brown or Sutton lime had been found south of the Canal and west of the village. The fumes and noise involved in this process would have added considerably to the general air of industrial activity in the village centre.

The Famous Clock

Although the Duke was generally a benevolent employer, he kept an eye on work in progress. On one occasion he noticed that workmen had not returned by 1-00pm from their "dinner" hour. When asked why they were late they protested that they could not hear the clock strike the single stroke at one. The Duke therefore arranged with an Eccles clockmaker called John Collier to alter the clock which was in a tower in the works yard, or make another, so that it struck thirteen at one o'clock. There were no excuses after that! The same clock, in a modified form, is now in the tower of St Mark's Church in Worsley where it can, if allowed, still strike thirteen at one o'clock.

Part 5:

The Underground Canals

Worsley Delph c.1766 - note massive crane used to move stone blocks (A.Young)

While all this work was going on above ground, miners were excavating underground canals or Navigable Levels from Worsley Delph northwards deep into the coal measures. The coal measures north of Worsley village were found to be at an angle of 16 degrees or 1:4. This meant that an underground canal driven northwards at the same level as the main surface canal would cut through many seams and because of faulting, it cut three of the

Rock was moved by blasting and picks and shovels.

best seams twice. If, when a seam was crossed, tunnels could be cut east and west from the northern leg of the main underground canal, along the strike of the seam, coal could be carried back to the main canal for transport out into the Delph and so to the waiting markets of Salford and Manchester.

The first tunnel entrance was dug at the western side of the Delph, roughly elliptical in shape, it had a diameter of about 2.4 metres (8 feet), with a water depth of 1.2 metres (4 feet). A further entrance tunnel was dug in 1770 about 27 metres (30 yards) to the east and the two tunnels met about 457 metres (500 yards) from their mouths in the Delph, at Waters Meet. Tunnelling was not always easy given the primitive tools in use at the time. Much of the rock was moved by blasting and picks and shovels were the main tools used to move the debris. Sometimes the rock was so hard that the men, who were on piece work, were almost in despair. They appealed to the Duke who is said to have produced his snuff box and, having taken out a pinch, said that so long as they could get out as much rock as that, they should keep going.

The Inclined Plane

The main level was eventually continued as far as Dixon Green in Farnworth, where a branch was dug to reach the Edgefold area of Deane in the west. Just south of Dixon Green, another branch stretched westwards as far as Wharton in Little Hulton and, at a later period, it connected with Brackley colliery in Middle Hulton. The land rises steadily north of Worsley village and the northernmost mine workings were 32 metres (35 yards) above the level of the horizontal main underground canal. To tap these higher workings another underground canal was built at a higher level and coal was at first lowered from it down shafts to the main canal.

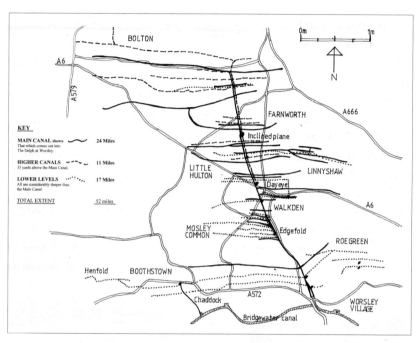

The final extent of the underground canals total length 52 miles (G.Atkinson)

In the early 1790s, an ingenious scheme was devised by John Gilbert. This was an Inclined Plane designed to allow the transport of loaded barges from the higher level canal to the main level without the need to unload the coal. It was built underneath Ashton Field about three quarters of a mile north of Walkden shopping centre and was completely underground.

In the early 1790s, an ingenious scheme was devised by John Gilbert.

It consisted of two locks on the higher level canal, separated by a metre thick brick wall, which were connected to the lower main canal by a tunnel in a natural rock slope of 1:4, 136 metres (150 yards) long. The tunnel was hollowed out from a 7.7 metres (25 feet) thick bed of rock. There were two locks and runways at the top which merged into one 52 metres (57 yards) from the bottom. A loaded boat entered one of the locks at the top where its stern was connected to a rope 65 millimeters in diameter, which ran round a large "jig" wheel (drum) with a vertical, toothed brake wheel set vertically at its midpoint and was then connected to the bow of an empty boat waiting at the foot of the slope, which continued two metres below the water level. When the plane was rebuilt at the beginning of the nineteenth century the brake wheel was changed to a horizontal position. The lock gate at the top was then closed and the water drained from the lock allowing

Worsley Old Hall from south east. The canal was planned in the rooms at the eastern end of the building

*Duke of Bridgewater's
Underground Plane at
Walkden Moor*

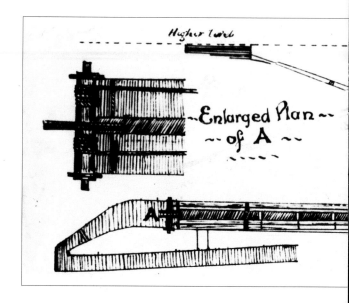

the full boat to settle on to a cradle, which
was on rollers and which ran on iron rails. The
loaded boat was then allowed to descend,
using the brake wheel as a windlass to start
it if necessary, and as it did so it dragged an
empty barge on to a submerged trolley waiting
at the bottom, on the bed of the canal, and so
up the "plane" into the top lock. The full boat
floated off the cradle at the bottom of the
slope on to the main canal and the top lock
was filled with water to allow the empty boat
access to the upper level.

*The whole plane was 138 metres (151 yards)
in length and 6 metres (20 feet) wide.*

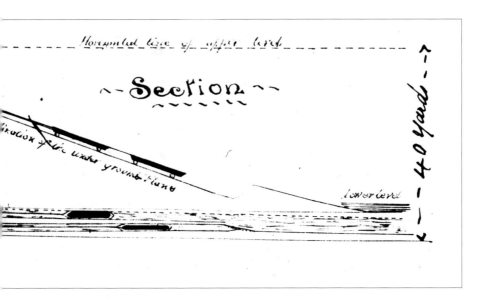

The whole plane was 138 metres (151 yards) in length and 6 metres (20 feet) wide. The cradles ran on cast iron rollers which had flanged ends to keep them on the track. Each cradle weighed about 5.6 tons an empty boat weighed about 4.5 tons and a full boat carried about 13.4 tons of coal therefore making a total weight of 23.5 tons. Thirty boats could be handled in eight hours so each transit took about fifteen minutes. The Plane was first used in 1797 and was still working in 1826.

John Gilbert's Death

Sadly, John Gilbert died in 1795 and so never saw his designs come to fruition. The remaining work was supervised by the Duke himself. John Gilbert had been in the Duke's employment for almost forty years and when he died, it is said in the Duke's arms, the Duke thought so much of him that he gave permission for him, and later his wife, to be buried in the Egerton family vault in Eccles Parish Church.

The Deeper Levels

The problem of getting newly built boats onto the higher level canal before the Inclined Plane was built was solved by constructing a tunnel called a "Day-eye" because it led to the surface, down which boats could be winched on a trolley. One was built underneath what is now the northern section of the car park in Walkden centre. There were also a number of independent Deep Levels cut below the main channel and coal mined in these was carried to a shaft and then lifted to the main level by means of ingenious cranes powered by counterweights of water. At Edgefold on Walkden Road a deepened shaft was able to serve three new levels. In total, something like fifty miles of underground canals were cut.

A number of methods for moving the boats along the canals were used. These included canvas slings to which a hook was attached which were worn by the boatmen round the waist or across the shoulders and hooked onto a ring in the roof of the canal. The boatman then pushed the boat forward with his feet as he walked backwards towards the stern of the

The boatman then pushed the boat forward with his feet as he walked backwards towards the stern.

44

mineboat or "starvationer" as they are now sometimes known, as the rough construction enables the internal ribs to be seen. In other parts there were hand-holes in the wall and in areas where the canal silted up rapidly, the boatmen lay on their backs and walked the boat along using the roof of the canal. On the main canal, low dams, known as "cloughs" or "clows" were used to close off a section which raised the water level behind them. When the "clows" were lowered, the flood of water helped propel the trains of boats along towards the open air.

1950s photograph of remains of the Inclined Plane

Part 6:

Visitors To The Canals

Soon after the news of the opening of the underground canals became widespread, they became objects of interest throughout Britain, Europe and North America. One of the early visitors was a Frenchman called Gabriel Jars who came in 1765. It was thought likely that he was an industrial spy, probably working on behalf of the French government. In 1768 King Christian VII of Denmark visited Worsley. He was supposed to be travelling incognito but, as he had a retinue of fifty courtiers with him and stayed at the Bull Hotel in Manchester, his assumed name of Travendahl made little difference. At Worsley the party was taken up the "level" in mine boats. Sadly there are no details of the visit but it was said that "His Majesty much enjoyed the greatness of the undertaking"; he also gave the boatmen "handsome tips".

His Majesty much enjoyed the greatness of the undertaking; he also gave the boatmen "handsome tips".

A more entertaining account was that of the visit of a "Lady Lucy" recorded in the London Chronicle for November 1765. She writes as follows "Having obtained a ticket to see this curiosity... by sending your name to a new house (the Brick Hall)... you encounter with lighted candles, the subterraneous passage in a boat... when you first enter the passage and when you come among the colliers your heart is apt to fail you... but should your spirits sink the company are ever ready to aid you with a glass of wine"; sadly more accurate details are missing. In later years Archdukes from Austria, a Russian Princess, the Grand Duke Nicholas, later Czar of Russia, local worthies and groups from learned organisations such as the British Association, all travelled into the mines by underground canal.

An account of a visit of a different kind to the underground canal was recorded in a Blackburn newspaper on 11th September 1793. It was headed "A wonderful escape at Worsley" and recorded how one Richard Withington of Manchester was out hunting one day in Worsley on horseback when he and his horse fell through an old mine or ventilation shaft ninety feet on to the canal. He was hardly hurt but his horse was killed and his hunting cap, "was so driven into a part of the tunnel that it required extraordinary force to pull it from between the stones". Apparently he was rescued by a boatman on the underground canal between Worsley and Mosley Common.

In Spring 1965 the author of this book was fortunate enough to have the opportunity to travel on the underground canal from the Ellesmere Pit in the middle of Walkden to Worsley Delph, with a maintenance party. It was pitch black apart from our helmet lights. We sat down one behind the other in a mine boat and pushed off. Progress was slow as so much silt had accumulated that the roof was very low. We "legged" it most of the way by walking along the roof. Where the rock

was sound, the canal was cut from the living rock but where there were shaley patches, the roof was covered in hand-made brick, still as sound as when they were laid about two hundred years ago. At "Water's Meet", about two hundred metres from the Delph, the junction was sculpted from solid rock into marvellous arches. After two and a half hours, we finally reached the Delph where we retired to the cottage for a cup of tea in exchange for a bag of coal collected en route from the old Edge Fold mine.

The End of an Era

The last sailing along the underground canal system was from the Ellesmere Pit in the middle of Walkden to Worsley Delph. It took place on the 28th September 1968. The last person to leave the pit before the filling of the shafts began was Jack Harrison of the National Coal Board. The filling in of the main shaft was completed on 11th November 1968. In 1998, a team from Selby and Mansfield entered the underground canal to conduct a survey as far as "Waters Meet" as part of the Steam, Coal and Canal Project on the Bridgewater Canal.

Although the horses had been specially trained, one reared and fell into the canal soon after leaving Patricroft.

The general condition of the air and tunnel were found to be good and their report formed part of a bid to the Heritage lottery Fund.

Queen Victoria visits Worsley

In later years illustrious passengers travelled along the Bridgewater Canal itself. In 1851 Queen Victoria and Prince Albert travelled by train to Patricroft station and then, in her own words, described her trip to Worsley. In her diary she wrote "it was a very elegant barge to which a rope was fastened, drawn by four horses. Ourselves, the ladies, Lady Brackley and her little boy, the old Duke (of Wellington) and Captain Egerton came into it with us. Half was entirely covered in; the other half had an awning over it... in half an hour we were at the landing place in Worsley Park and in five minutes at the Hall door"(The New Hall). The barge was specially built for the occasion and although the horses had been specially trained, one reared and fell into the canal soon after leaving Patricroft. The horse was retrieved and the journey continued. A little further on the tow rope snapped causing a further delay. Queen Victoria however made no mention of these incidents in her diary of the day. Queens did not notice such things!

The arrival of Queen Victoria at Worsley 1851 - the New Hall can be seen in the distance (London Illustrated News)

*The Queen's Barge
- later used by the
Earl of Ellesmere
(Mullineux Collection)*

Passenger Transport

It has to be remembered that the Bridgewater Canal network was something new in the transport business. Although coal was the main product carried on some sections of the waterway, other commodities such as cotton, grain, timber, lime and other raw materials were also important items that were carried. Not least of the items conveyed were people. Before the coming of the railways the canals were a quick and comfortable means for getting from one place to another.

The fare from Manchester to Worsley was 1/-s (5p) or 6d (2½p) for "steerage" passengers and refreshments were served on board on the longer journeys.

Passenger barge pulled by horses at speed

Passenger services began in 1769. The first boats were converted barges but it was not long before new, purpose built, vessels were being used. By 1774 there were two, each of which could carry about one hundred passengers. An excellent description of these boats was given by a German engineer. He wrote; "One cannot travel more pleasantly, in more comfort or more cheaply than in these boats. Their length is 17 metres (56 feet) their width 2.5 metres (8 feet) and the height inside at the centre is 2 metres (7 feet). At the top of the deck stands a post on which is hooked the towing rope which is drawn by a horse, at the foot of this post lies a pulley block and tackle whereby a sail can be hoisted by the boatman at the helm, and can be held in the desired direction. The boat goes at 5 English miles per hour... the journey from Runcorn to Manchester being completed in eight hours. The charge per person for the whole journey in the general quarters is 2/3d (11p) and 3/6d (17p) in special accommodation". The bows of the vessel were fitted with curved, sharpened sabres which could cut the tow lines of barges slow to get out of their way and a liveried postilion complete with horn to warn of approach, rode the leading horse. The fare from Manchester to Worsley was 1/-s (5p) or 6d (2½p) for "steerage" passengers and refreshments were served on board on the longer journeys.

The Canal boats continued into the nineteenth century but with greatly reduced fares to compete with the railway. Something like a small railway station was built at Castlefield and to cater for holiday traffic, boats ran from Manchester via Wigan to Scarisbrick on the Leeds-Liverpool Canal from where passengers continued by coach to Southport. In 1843, "Swift" boats were introduced pulled by specially bred horses which could pull a passenger boat from Altrincham to Manchester in less than one hour. In 1850 it cost just 6d to travel from Manchester to Liverpool. In Worsley, boats landed their passengers at the Packet House steps in the centre of the village. This building takes its name from the carriage of "packets", usually of mail, although there is no evidence that letters were ever transported to Worsley in this way.

Specially bred horses could pull a passenger boat from Altrincham to Manchester in less than one hour.

The Packet House and steps Worsley, about 1910. The black and white work was added about 1850

Packet boat return ticket from Dunham to Manchester

Part 7:

The Duke's Other Interests

It would be wrong to assume that the Duke spent all his time in Worsley, in fact it has been suggested that he was only in Worsley ten times between 1759 and 1762 and then only for short periods of perhaps about two weeks at a time. He spent the rest of his time travelling between his various estates checking on their finances and often borrowing money where possible. His undertakings were many and varied. Wool came from the Ashridge estate and was sold in Lancashire, beef cattle were driven from as far as West Scotland and went to London via Ashridge. Chat Moss, near Worsley was reclaimed using colliery waste so that crops of barley, wheat, potatoes and hay could be grown.

In 1797 a steamboat made the journey from Runcorn to Castlefield.

Steam Boat Trials

This was a time of experiment in many directions and in 1793 a steamboat was tried out on the Sankey Navigation and in 1797 a steamboat made the journey from Runcorn to Castlefield along the Bridgewater Canal. In 1796 plans to build a boat with a paddle wheel at the stern which was driven by steam were sent to Bateman and Sherratt, engineers of Salford. They made the boilers, gears and shaft while the hull was made in the Duke's Worsley workshops; the paddles were made by the Duke's foreman millwright also in Worsley. Some

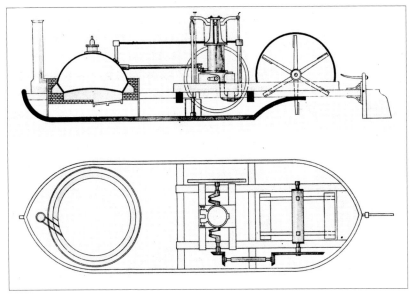

"Plan & section of a steam boat & engine for His Grace the Duke of Bridgewater, erected and set to work 1799"

say that an American engineer called Fulton
interested the Duke in the scheme, but the
boat was probably designed by the Duke and
Captain Shanks RN., a well known inventor.
It was a curious looking vessel. It had a tall
funnel in the bows, then came a large domed
boiler and then came a host of driving rods
and a large vertical flywheel through which
the helmsman had to peer. It was said that
the local people detested the craft so much
that they christened it 'Bonaparte' and there
was great delight when, on its maiden voyage,
the funnel proved too tall to get under the
Canal bridges. The funnel had to be hinged.
The Bonaparte did however manage to pull
eight 25 ton mine boats at a speed of one mile
per hour to Manchester. It was no faster than
horses and there were fears that the paddles
might disturb the puddled clay on the bed of
the canal causing it to leak, so the experiment
was abandoned. Just before the Duke died he

*Everyone wanted to invest money in canals which, by then,
had become an outstandingly good investment.*

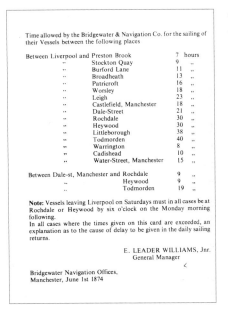

Sailing timetable

ordered eight boats to a more successful design by William Symington for Lord Dundas, but after his death the order was cancelled. Bonaparte's engine was removed and used as a pumping engine in local collieries for almost one hundred years.

Financial Success

It took until 1783 before the great Canal undertaking could be said to be a financial success and in that year the Duke gave a bonus of a guinea (£1.05p) to each collier and half a guinea to each drawer who had been in the Duke's service for at least a year. After 1783 it began to be possible to start repaying the very many loans and by 1793, everyone wanted to invest money in canals which, by then, had become an outstandingly good investment.

Part 8:

The Duke In Later Life

By the late 1770s Francis 3rd Duke of Bridgewater, was well known throughout Lancashire. The cheaper and more plentiful coal carried by his Canal had meant increased prosperity for industry and lower unemployment. He was not interested in his appearance and usually wore an old fashioned suit of brown worsted consisting of a jacket and breeches fastened at the knee with a pair of silver buckles; he also wore a tricorn hat. He was about five feet nine inches in height and had an extremely florid complexion "not from the effects of liquor but such as we formerly saw in a fine, stout healthy farmer". As the Duke got older gout became a major problem. People complained that he rarely washed and therefore stank and he increasingly disliked women. He also took snuff and was rarely seen without a churchwarden pipe in his mouth. Despite these problems, his charitable works and the employment which his undertakings had brought about, meant that he was much loved by ordinary people throughout Lancashire.

People complained that he rarely washed and therefore stank and he increasingly disliked women.

Francis Egerton, 3rd Duke of Bridgewater in old age (Mullineux Collection)

During the 1790s his coach arrived one day in Manchester from the south with tired horses. He was cheered down the streets and eventually his horses were unhitched and his coach was dragged all the way to the Brick Hall in Worsley by the onlookers. Many anecdotes about him have been told all speaking of his good humour and understanding where the workforce was concerned. A typical one concerns when he asked a workman why he was late for work one morning. The man explained that his wife had had a baby during the night. The Duke replied "Aye, well, we have to take what the good Lord sends us". The workman said "Aye well, I notice he sends all th' babbies to our house and all th' brass to yourn". The Duke laughed and gave him a guinea.

The Duke's Death

The Duke died at about 3.30am on the 8th of March 1803; he was 67 years old. A coach accident in London appears to have lead to a severe bout of influenza from which he never recovered. He asked for a simple funeral but

The Duke died at about 3.30am on the 8th of March 1803.

it was not to be. There was a hearse with six black horses, the Duke's own carriage pulled by six horses; three coach loads of mourners each pulled by six horses; ten outriders and the usual collection of mute mourners. He was buried in the churchyard at Little Gaddesden, near Ashridge in Hertfordshire.

The Duke's Will

The Duke's will was one of the most complicated ever written. As he died childless most of the estates were to go to his cousin as laid down in his father's will. The estates in Lancashire and Cheshire, including Worsley, and the Brackley estate in Northamptonshire, were to be placed in trust for his nephew George Granville Leveson-Gower (pronounced Loosen-Gore), Marquis of Stafford. The Dukedom died with the Canal Duke. Leveson-Gower was to receive the revenue from the estates while he lived and on his death, it would pass to his second son Francis on condition that Francis would change his name to Egerton when he inherited.

The Bridgewater Trust, as it was known, was set up to manage the estate and was to last until twenty one years after the deaths of all the peers of the realm and their eldest sons alive in 1803. The Trust lasted exactly one hundred years, expiring in 1903.

The Trust was to be run by three Trustees and the Duke chose Robert Haldane Bradshaw to be the resident Superintendent Trustee at a salary of £2,000 per year. Bradshaw had become Chief Agent to the estates in 1800, following Thomas Gilbert.

Monuments to the Duke

There are few monuments to the great Canal Duke. A tall stone column in his honour was set up in the park at Ashridge by his cousin and in Worsley, when the works yard was demolished in 1903, the base of an elaborate chimney was converted into a drinking fountain approached by steps around its base. A Latin inscription, in praise of the Duke, was inscribed on the risers of these steps where they can still be seen, on the monument, on Worsley Green. It is not known who wrote the lines but a number of translations have been attempted, often in verse, and the following is a translation made by Captain Henry Hart Davis, who was Chief Agent of the Bridgewater estates and the main instigator of Worsley Green, as a residential area, in 1905.

A Latin inscription, in praise of the Duke, was inscribed on the risers of these steps where they can still be seen, on the monument, on Worsley Green.

Monument, at Worsley Green and translation of Latin inscription

"A lofty column breathing smoke and fire,
Did I the Builder's glory once aspire,
Whose founder was that Duke who far and wide
Bridged water through Bridgewater's countryside.

Stranger! This spot, where once did never cease
Great Vulcan's year, would sleep in silent peace,
But beneath my very stones does mount
That waters source, his honour's spring and fount.

Alas! That I who gazed o'er field and town,
Should to these base proportions dwindle down.
But all's not over, still enough remains
To testify past glories, duties, pains."

Part 9:

The Coming Of The Railways

A few years before the Duke's death he began to be concerned about the growing threat from what he called "those damned tramways" and after his death, the threat materialised. In 1825 a bill was put forward to obtain permission for a railway from Liverpool to Manchester. At first it was strongly opposed by the Bridgewater Trustees because of the threat it posed to their near monopoly grip on transport in the area. Their opposition was however withdrawn when they were given 1,000 shares and allowed to appoint three directors to the railway board. At the same time, Leveson-Gower bought £100,000 worth of shares in the projected railway which, by 1829, were worth £173,000.

Despite 170 Parliamentary skirmishes to try to preserve the interests of the Canal against the railway promoters, railway development became inevitable.

It was not until 1861 that the railway from Eccles was allowed to reach Worsley.

Lord Francis Egerton

The Francis Leveson-Gower mentioned in the Duke's will, duly changed his name, as required, to Francis Egerton and as Lord Francis Egerton came to Worsley in 1837. In 1846, the year that Lord Francis Egerton was created Earl of Ellesmere, the promoters of the Manchester-Altrincham railway wanted to cross Castlefield on a viaduct. This was allowed after Lord Francis Egerton was allotted 10,000 shares in the company and in exchange agreed to try to end the sailing of passenger boats from Manchester to Broadheath.

The Sale of the Canal

It was not until 1861 that the railway from Eccles was allowed to reach Worsley. The Directors of the railway company made a gesture by travelling to Worsley by Canal. Railways continued to develop in Cheshire and the expense involved in maintaining and developing the Worsley coalfields meant that there was little money available to fight this competition. In 1872, the Trustees were finally advised to sell their canals to the Manchester, Sheffield and Lincolnshire Railway Co., which were soon to amalgamate with the Midland Railway Co. The sale took place for £1,115,000. The news of the sale caused consternation in Worsley as so many people depended upon the estate for jobs. In 1874 this became the Bridgewater Navigation Co. Ltd and in 1887 the company was bought by the Manchester Ship Canal Co. this time for £1,710,000 to get access to lands along the Irwell and Mersey. Sadly, because of the need for access to the sea along the new Ship Canal for sea-going vessels opened in 1894, Brindley and Gilbert's stone Aqueduct had to be demolished and replaced by a swing aqueduct which is still in use today.

Despite competition from the railways, by 1860 the Canals were still carrying three times as much cargo as they had in 1833 and when the Manchester Ship Canal Co. bought the Bridgewater it was laid down that it must be kept open and in good repair.

The End of Commercial Traffic

By 1940 the Bridgewater Canal was still carrying nearly one million tons a year and was financially profitable until the 1960s. After that date with the closure of the coal mines, the closure of the Barton power station and the rise of motor transport, leisure activities overtook commercial usage and there is now no commercial traffic on the Canal.

Leisure activities overtook commercial usage.

Liverpool-Manchester railway crossing the Bridgewater Canal at Patricroft Bridge (1830s). First class passengers did have some cover from the weather

Part 10:

The Delph And Canal Today

One of the best known features of the Canal at Worsley has been its colour. It used to be bright orange from the ochre which leached out from the coal measures via the underground canals. This colour has always

Packet House, Worsley

Now the Canal has become a muddy shade of green permanently.

appeared something of an embarrassment to the Local Authority so much so that when Her Majesty the Queen and the Duke of Edinburgh visited Worsley in May 1968, there was an attempt to dye the Canal blue. Unfortunately when the blue dye met the orange of the ochre the resultant colour was a sickly shade of green!

Attempts to Clean the Water

Now the Canal has become a muddy shade of green permanently. This is due to the fact that, in the early years of this century, the Environment Agency expressed concern that the ochre (iron oxide) in the Delph which had come out from the underground canal, could possibly harm its flora and fauna. As a result of this, in 2001, the Coal Authority which is responsible for the underground canals, began consultation on

Barton swing Aqueduct a scheme to remedy the problem. The work was completed by 2004. The Delph is now a scheduled Ancient Monument so strict controls were imposed before remedial work could begin. The scheme has involved piping water directly from the underground canal so that no water now directly reaches the Delph. The piped water goes by underground pipeline one kilometre to the west where, in a building disguised as a barn, the water is aerated and then allowed to

settle in a lagoon. The water then passes in to two specially planted reed beds where the silt is filtered out. The now almost clear water is then pumped back into the Canal. There is still however a vast deposit of ochre on the bed of the Delph which is not affected by the present scheme and this awaits further action.

Packet House, Worsley

Canal side at Worsley

New developments along the bank

The Bridgewater Canal Today

The Bridgewater Canal is operated by the Bridgewater Canal Company, part of the Peel Group. Peel is responsible for the running, maintenance and repair of the Canal and the management of the various activities that take place upon it, including boating, fishing and walking along its tow path. It has a long term programme of improvements, which have been planned to enhance the facilities on the Canal (such as new marinas) and encourage greater use by the public. Since 1975, the Bridgewater Canal Trust, which is made up from all the Local Authorities through which the Canal

To date, around one third of the Canal towpath has been improved, providing an enhanced multi-use route.

passes, has assisted the Company by helping them to deliver these services and enhance the Canal experience for their residents. The Trust meets twice a year to discuss the amenity benefits of the Canal and ensure co-ordination with the interests of the wider community along its length.

In recent times, the Trust has been supportive of the Bridgewater Way project, an £8 million scheme to enhance and improve the Bridgewater Canal towpath for users and the local community. To date, around one third of the Canal towpath has been improved, providing an enhanced multi-use route.

The Company also holds regular meetings with local interest and user groups to ensure that any concerns or suggestions concerning the operation of the Canal can be considered. With this mix of users and Local Authorities helping to guide its future, there is little doubt that this famous waterway will continue to be a wonderful recreational asset for many years to come.

Humpback Bridge, Worsley Village

© John Aldred, Worsley 2011

Further details regarding the Bridgewater Canal today can be found on the following websites

www.peel.co.uk   www.bridgewatercanal.co.uk

THE PEEL GROUP

Part 11:

Sources And Further Reading

Sources and Further Reading

1. Frank Mullineux "The Duke of Bridgewater's Canal" 2nd edition, Eccles and District History Society 1988

2. Glen Atkinson "The Canal Duke's Collieries, Worsley 1760-1900", Neil Richardson 1982

3. Hugh Malet "Bridgewater - the Canal Duke 1736-1803", Manchester University Press 1977

4. Christopher Grayling "The Bridgewater Heritage" Bridgewater Estates PLC 1983

5. John Aldred "Worsley in 1807", Salford City Council Heritage Service 2004

6. Ann Monaghan(ed) "Journeys on the Underground Canal 1765-1968", Salford City Libraries 1998

7. John Aldred "Worsley - an Historical Geography", Worsley Civic Trust 1988

8. F.C. Mather "After the Canal Duke", Oxford University Press 1970

9. Bernard Falk "The Bridgewater Millions", Hutchinson & Co 1942

10. Peter Lead "Agents of Revolution", University of Keele 1989

All the above and more may be seen at Salford Local History Library, Peel Park.

Edge illustrations on pages 6-14 from pre-canal map of Worsley; pages 26-36 from Foulkes map 1785; pages 44-66 from first edition O.S.1846.

WORSLEY, Nov. 11, 1837.

SIR,

I have to request that Directions may be given, to enforce Mr. Bradshaw's REGULATION against Flatmen's and Lightermen's WIVES living and sleeping on board with their Husbands.

In explanation of this Order, I want it to be stated, that the existence of such a practice, besides affording many excuses for depredation, leads to a system of Morals extremely detrimental and therefore to be avoided.

I am, your obedient Servant,

JAMES LOCH.

G. S. FEREDAY SMITH, Esq.
Bridgewater Canal Office,
Manchester.

Letter of request of James Loch

FARES

	FRONT ROOM	s.	d.	BACK ROOM	s.	d.
To	Stretford	1	0		0	6
To	Altrincham	1	0		0	9
To	Dunham	1	0		1	0
To	Lymm	2	0		1	3
To	London-bridge	2	6		1	6
To	Preston	3	0		2	0
To	Runcorn	3	6		2	3
To	Worsley	1	0		0	6
To	And from Worsley	1	6		0	9

Fares by passenger boat on the Bridgewater Canal